Notre Dame Fighting Irish Trivia Quiz Book

500 Questions on All Things Blue and Gold

Chris Bradshaw

St Cyprian Books

Book Cover by HeadfuzzbyGrimboid

First edition 2023

CONTENTS

INTRODUCTION

Think you know about the Notre Dame Fighting Irish? Put your knowledge to the test with this collection of quizzes on all things blue and gold.

The book covers the whole history of the program, from the groundbreaking successes of Knute Rockne, through multiple National Championships, right up to the team led by Marcus Freeman today.

The biggest names in Fighting Irish history are present and correct so look out for questions on Tim Brown, Brady Quinn, Michael Mayer, Tony Rice, Joe Montana, Rocket Ismail and many, many more. There are 500 questions in all covering running backs and receivers, coaches and quarterbacks, pass rushers and punters and much else besides.

Each quiz contains a selection of 20 questions and is either a mixed bag of pot luck testers or is centered on a specific category such as the 1988 National Champions or Irish Stars in the NFL. There are easy, medium and hard questions offering something for Notre Dame novices as well as professors of Irish history.

You'll find the answers to each quiz below the following quiz. For example, the answers to Quiz 1: Pot Luck are underneath Quiz 2: Quarterbacks. The only exception is Quiz 25: Pot Luck. The answers to these questions can be found under the Quiz 1 questions.

All statistics and records are accurate up to the start of the 2023 season. Good luck!

QUIZ 1 POT LUCK

1. What color are the numbers on the Notre Dame colored jersey?

2. Whom did Marcus Freeman succeed as the Notre Dame head coach?

3. What is the name of the Notre Dame fight song?

4. The Rip Miller Trophy is awarded to the winner of games between Notre Dame and which opponent?

5. Whose 2,099 career receiving yards are the most by a Notre Dame tight end?

6. Do the Irish have an all-time winning or losing record in games against opponents from the SEC?

7. Which stud offensive lineman was named the MVP of the 2013 Pinstripe Bowl against Rutgers?

8. Which former Notre Dame star was named the AP NFL Offensive Rookie of the Year 1993 after rushing for 1,429 yards and 7 TDs with the Rams?

9. True or false – Notre Dame has never lost to Navy in back-to-back seasons?

10. Which trio of receivers each passed the 100-yard mark in the Fiesta Bowl against Oklahoma State on New Year's Day 2002?

11. The Irish secured the 1973 National Championship after defeating which SEC powerhouse in the Sugar Bowl?

12. What was the final score in that classic 1973 National Championship decider?

13. In 2006, who became just the second Notre Dame quarterback to win the Johnny Unitas Golden Arm Award?

14. True or false – Up to end of the 2022 season the Irish were unbeaten in games in the Shamrock Series?

15. What is the nickname given to the group of fans who devotedly follow Notre Dame despite never attending or graduating from the school?

16. The Seattle Seahawks used the second overall pick of the 1993 NFL Draft to select which Notre Dame quarterback?

17. Which Notre Dame back tore his ACL, MCL and LCL in a 2011 game against Boston College but overcame that adversity to win a Super Bowl ring with the New England Patriots?

18. Tim Brown scored back-to-back punt return touchdowns in a 1988 game against which opponent?

19. How old was Marcus Freeman when he was appointed Notre Dame's head coach? a) 36 b) 37 c) 38

20. Who holds the record for the most punts in a season with 78? a) Joey Hildbold b) Blair Kiel c) Ben Turk

Quiz 25 Answers

1. Jarious Jackson 2. Life, sweetness, hope 3. Navy 4. Gray 5. Tyler Eifert 6. Oklahoma 7. Matt Shelton 8. Terrail Lambert 9. Rutgers 10. True 11. Bob Golic 12. A green shamrock 13. Joe Theismann 14. Soldier Field 15. Chris Tyree 16. Tony Rice 17. Drew Brees 18. True 19. c) Texas A&M 20. c) Mules

QUIZ 2 QUARTERBACKS

1. Who is Notre Dame's all-time leader in passing yards?

2. Who holds the school record for the most 300-yard passing games in a single season?

3. Brady Quinn is one of two Fighting Irish quarterbacks to throw more than 30 touchdown passes in a season. Who is the other?

4. Whose 3,919 passing yards are the most by a Notre Dame quarterback in a single season?

5. In 2012, which quarterback opened his career by leading the Irish to 10 straight wins?

6. Who holds the record for the most rushing yards in a season by a Notre Dame quarterback?

7. Who were the two Notre Dame quarterbacks to throw a touchdown pass during the 2022 season?

8. Who holds the record for the most touchdown passes in a single game?

9. How many touchdown passes did he throw to set that record?

10. Which Notre Dame quarterback spent three seasons playing in the Canadian Football League before returning to the NFL to win a Super Bowl and a League MVP award?

11. In which round of the 1979 NFL Draft did the San Francisco 49ers select Notre Dame quarterback Joe Montana?

12. In 1970, who became the first Notre Dame quarterback to throw for more than 500 yards in a single game?

13. Who became the second Notre Dame player to break the 500-yard barrier in a New Year's Day 2022 game against Oklahoma State?

14. Whose 30 wins as a starter are the most by a Fighting Irish quarterback?

15. Who set a school record in a 2014 game against Syracuse after completing 25 straight passes?

16. Who holds the school record for throwing the most interceptions in a single season?

17. Which quarterback threw 59 touchdown passes between 2010 and 2013 but scored just a single rushing touchdown?

18. Whose 23 career rushing touchdowns are the most by a Notre Dame quarterback?

19. Who holds the record for the most successive passes without throwing an interception? a) Ian Book b) Jimmy Clausen c) Brady Quinn

20. How many passes did he throw to set that record? a) 246 b) 256 c) 266

Quiz 1 Answers

1. White with gold trim 2. Brian Kelly 3. Notre Dame Victory March 4. Navy 5. Michael Mayer 6. Winning 7. Zack Martin 8. Jerome Bettis 9. False 10. Kevin Austin, Lorenzo Styles and Chris Tyree 11. Alabama 12. Irish 24-23 Crimson Tide 13. Brady Quinn 14. True 15. Subway Alumni 16. Rick Mirer 17. Jonas Gray 18. Michigan State 19. 36 years old 20. a) Joey Hildbold

QUIZ 3 POT LUCK

1. The Shillelagh Trophy is awarded to the winner of games between Notre Dame and which opponent?

2. In what country was former star receiver Chase Claypool born and raised?

3. The Irish usually play five games a year against opponents from which conference?

4. True or false – The Irish have had fewer than 10 losing seasons throughout their history?

5. Do the Irish have an all-time winning or losing record in games against USC?

6. True or false – The Irish rushed 91 times for 597 yards in a 1969 game against Navy?

7. Which Notre Dame star was the only player to win the Heisman Trophy from a team that had a losing record?

8. Which rusher scored a touchdown in a 1993 game against Michigan despite being knocked unconscious during the play?

9. The 1993 movie 'Rudy' told the story of which inspirational Notre Dame player?

10. In 1971, who became the first African-American to start at quarterback for the Irish?

11. 'The Gipper' was the nickname of which Notre Dame great?

12. Which Notre Dame receiver and future NFL star was drafted by the Arizona Diamondbacks and the San Francisco Giants in the 2007 and 2010 MLB Drafts?

13. Which tandem both passed the 100 rushing yards barrier in 2020 games against Florida State and Syracuse?

14. Which head coach steered the Irish to the 1973 National Championship?

15. Inspired by his football career, which former Irish tight end wrote the 2008 novel, 'Rough and Tumble'?

16. 'Mr. Fling' was the nickname of which 1960s era Notre Dame quarterback?

17. And which receiver was known as 'Mr. Cling'?

18. True or false – During the 1952 season the Irish created 51 opposition fumbles?

19. Who holds the record for the most career touchdown passes? a) Ian Book b) Brady Quinn c) Joe Theismann

20. How many touchdown passes did he throw to set that record? a) 76 b) 86 c) 96

Quiz 2 Answers

1. Brady Quinn 2. Jimmy Clausen 3. Ian Book 4. Brady Quinn 5. Everett Golson 6. Tony Rice 7. Drew Pyne and Tyler Buchner 8. Brady Quinn 9. Six 10. Joe Theismann 11. Third 12. Joe Theismann 13. Jack Coan 14. Ian Book 15. Everett Golson 16. Steve Beuerlein 17. Tommy Rees 18. Tony Rice 19. a) Ian Book 20. c) 266 passes

Quiz 4 Running Backs

1. Whose 4,318 career rushing yards are the most by a Notre Dame running back?

2. Who holds the record for the most rushing yards by an Irish back in a single season?

3. Who set a school record in 2003 after rushing for 262 yards in a game against Pittsburgh?

4. Which back rushed for 2,153 yards and 27 touchdowns between 2019 and 2021 including back-to-back 1,000 yard seasons in 2020 and 2021?

5. In 2015, who set the school record for the most rushing yards by a running back in his freshman season?

6. 'The Bus' was the nickname of which legendary Notre Dame back?

7. Who rushed for a team-best 920 yards and 11 touchdowns during the 2022 season?

8. In 1992, who became the first (and so far, only) Irish back to rush for more than 150 yards in a Bowl Game?

9. Of backs with at least 1,500 career rushing yards, who has the best yards per carry average? (clue: he played from 1989 until 1992)

10. Whose 56 catches in 2006 are the most by a Notre Dame running back in a single season?

11. With 49 career rushing touchdowns who is Notre Dame's highest-scoring back?

12. What is the most rushing touchdowns scored by a player in a single season?

13. Who are the co-holders of that rushing touchdowns record set in 1979 and 1984 respectively?

14. Whose 22 career 100-yard rushing games are the most by an Irish back?

15. Who holds the record for the most career receptions by a Notre Dame running back?

16. In 1993, who set a school record after rushing for more than 100 yards in six straight games?

17. Which back broke the 200-yard barrier three times during the 2003 season?

18. In 2017, who became just the second Irish back to rush for more than 200 yards in a game more than once in a single season?

19. How long is the longest rushing touchdown in school history? a) 97 yards b) 98 yards c) 99 yards

20. Who scored that record breaking touchdown run against Wake Forest in 2015? a) Josh Adams b) DeShone Kizer c) C.J. Prosise

Quiz 3 Answers

1. Purdue 2. Canada 3. Atlantic Coast Conference (ACC) 4. False 5. Winning 6. True 7. Paul Hornung 8. Reggie Brooks 9. Daniel 'Rudy' Ruettiger 10. Cliff Brown 11. George Gipp 12. Golden Tate 13. Kyren Williams and Chris Tyree 14. Ara Parseghian 15. Mark Bavaro 16. Terry Hanratty 17. Jim Seymour 18. True 19. b) Brady Quinn 20. c) 96 TDs

Quiz 5 Pot Luck

1. What color is the Notre Dame helmet?

2. Is the field at Notre Dame Stadium made of grass or artificial turf?

3. Which quarterback rushed for a school record 207 yards in a 2017 game at Boston College?

4. What five-word phrase appears on a sign that Notre Dame players traditionally tap as they exit the locker room?

5. By what nickname was explosive receiver Raghib Ismail commonly known?

6. Does Notre Dame have a winning or losing record in games played at neutral venues?

7. True or false – No jersey number has been retired by Notre Dame?

8. Which Notre Dame quarterback, and future Super Bowl winner, finished second in the voting for the 1970 Heisman Trophy?

9. Notre Dame was crowned 1977 National Champion after routing which #1 ranked opponent 38-10 in the Cotton Bowl?

10. Which junior quarterback led the Irish to that National Championship glory?

11. 'The Golden Boy' was the nickname of which Notre Dame all-time great?

12. True or false – In a 1965 game against Michigan State the Irish rushed 31 times for a total of -12 yards?

13. Which running back ensured his place in Irish folklore after returning a kickoff for a 93-yard touchdown in the 1973 National Championship Game?

14. Which tight end was picked by the Cowboys in round 2 of the 2006 Draft and went on to appear in 180 NFL games catching 299 passes and scoring 36 touchdowns?

15. True or false – 1960s receiver Jack Snow is the father of former MLB star J.T. Snow?

16. If all the opponents Notre Dame has faced throughout its history were listed alphabetically which team would be last on the list?

17. True or false – The Irish were unbeaten in games against USC with Lou Holtz as head coach?

18. Who booted a 51-yard field goal as time expired to give the Irish a famous 29-27 win over Michigan in 1980?

19. What is the most interceptions the Irish defense has registered in a single season? a) 28 b) 29 c) 30

20. The longest winning streak in school history stretched to how many games? a) 22 b) 23 c) 24

Quiz 4 Answers

1. Autry Denson 2. Vagas Ferguson 3. Allen Pinkett 4. Kyren Williams 5. Josh Adams 6. Jerome Bettis 7. Audric Estime 8. Jerome Bettis 9. Reggie Brooks 10. Darius Walker 11. Allen Pinkett 12. 17 touchdowns 13. Vagas Fergusson and Allen Pinkett 14. Autry Denson 15. Armando Allen 16. Lee Becton 17. Julius Jones 18. Josh Adams 19. b) 98 yards 20. a) Josh Adams

QUIZ 6 RECEIVERS

1. Who is Notre Dame's all-time leader in receiving yards?

2. Whose 1,496 receiving yards are the most by a Notre Dame receiver in a single season?

3. Which longtime Minnesota Viking holds the record for the most receiving yards in a game by a Notre Dame tight end?

4. Michael Floyd is one of two Irish receivers with 30 or more career receiving touchdowns. Who is the other?

5. Who holds the school record for the most catches in a season by a Notre Dame tight end?

6. Which Irish star was the first wide receiver to win the Heisman Trophy?

7. Which future NFL star's 140 career receptions between 2009 and 2012 are the second most by a Notre Dame tight end?

8. Who is the only Irish receiver with more than 200 career catches?

9. Who is the only Irish receiver to have multiple 200-yard receiving games?

10. Which receiver, who caught 157 passes between 1969 and 1971 was the first African-American named a team captain at Notre Dame?

11. Which longtime MLB pitcher caught 179 passes for 2,593 yards and 27 touchdowns in his college football career at South Bend?

12. Who is the only Notre Dame receiver to break the 100-yard barrier nine times in a single season?

13. Whose 10 catches in the 2003 Gator Bowl against NC State are the most by a Notre Dame receiver in a Bowl Game?

14. Who tied a school record after catching four touchdown passes in a 2019 game against Navy?

15. Whose 81-yard grab on New Year's Day 2016 against Ohio State in the Fiesta Bowl is the longest catch by an Irish player in a Bowl Game?

16. Which former Notre Dame superstar was named the MVP of the 1991 CFL Grey Cup for the Toronto Argonauts?

17. Who set a school record after catching 14 passes in a 2005 game against SMU?

18. Who is the only player in school history to catch 100 passes in a season?

19. Which Notre Dame receiver is the son of a three-time Mr. World body-building champion? a) Miles Boykin b) Will Fuller c) Equanimeous St. Brown

20. Who holds the school record after catching a touchdown pass in eight straight games? a) Tim Brown b) Jeff Samardzija c) Golden Tate

Quiz 5 Answers

1. Gold 2. Artificial turf 3. Brandon Wimbush 4. Play Like a Champion Today 5. Rocket 6. Winning 7. True 8. Joe Theismann 9. Texas 10. Joe Montana 11. Paul Hornung 12. True 13. Al Hunter 14. Anthony Fasano 15. True 16. Wisconsin 17. False – They went 9-1-1 18. Harry Oliver 19. b) 29 interceptions 20. b) 23 games

QUIZ 7 POT LUCK

1. What is the mascot of the Fighting Irish?

2. The Irish and which opponent compete for the Megaphone Trophy?

3. Who was the first Notre Dame pass catcher to break the 1,000-yard receiving barrier in back-to-back seasons?

4. The longest losing streak in school history was in 1960 and stretched to how many games?

5. Does Notre Dame have an all-time winning or losing record in games against Michigan?

6. Notre Dame reached the College Football Playoff for the first time in 2018, losing 30-3 in the semifinal to which opponent?

7. Best known as a 1,000-yard rusher, which versatile Irish star also played at defensive back, famously intercepting a pass in the 1990 season opener against Michigan?

8. Which quarterback, in his final appearance for Notre Dame, helped the Irish overturn a 17-point fourth quarter deficit to beat USC 38-37 in the 1986 season finale?

9. True or false – Gerry Faust had only ever coached in high school before being appointed the head coach of Notre Dame?

10. In 1998, the Irish defeated which opponent 39-36 in a game that included three defensive touchdowns, four blocked kicks, a kick return touchdown and an intentional safety?

11. What does the C in the name of former running back C.J. Prosise stand for?

12. Which former Irish star caught two touchdowns and rushed for another in San Francisco's Super Bowl XXIX win over the Chargers?

13. In 2017, the Irish rushed 51 times for 515 yards in a game against which rival?

14. The Irish suffered a shock 26-21 loss to which opponent in week two of the 2022 season despite going into the game as a 20.5-point favorite?

15. With 752 rushing yards and 10 TDs who was Notre Dame's top running back during the 1973 National Championship season?

16. Who had more passing yards while the quarterback at Notre Dame – Joe Theismann or Joe Montana?

17. Who was the first Notre Dame back to rush for more than 1,000 yards in three different seasons?

18. Does Notre Dame have a winning or losing record in games against Stanford?

19. What is the capacity of Notre Dame Stadium? a) 77,622 b) 78,622 c) 79,622

20. Between 1946 and 1950 the Irish went unbeaten for how many games? a) 37 b) 38 c) 39

Quiz 6 Answers

1. Michael Floyd 2. Golden Tate 3. Kyle Rudolph 4. Will Fuller 5. Michael Mayer 6. Tim Brown 7. Tyler Eifert 8. Michael Floyd 9. Golden Tate 10. Tom Gatewood 11. Jeff Samardzija 12. Golden Tate 13. Arnaz Battle 14. Chase Claypool 15. Will Fuller 16. Raghib Ismail 17. Maurice Stovall 18. Michael Floyd 19. c) Equanimeous St. Brown 20. b) Jeff Samardzija

QUIZ 8 DEFENSE

1. Which dominant Notre Dame defensive end won two National Championships in the 1970s as well as the Outland Trophy, Maxwell Award and Lombardi Award?

2. Which pass rusher registered double-digit sacks in both the 2021 and 2022 seasons?

3. Which future two-time Super Bowl winner is the only Notre Dame pass rusher to register four sacks in a game more than once?

4. Whose 10 interceptions in 1972 are the most by a Notre Dame player in a single season?

5. Which legendary Notre Dame defender registered more than 150 tackles in each of the 1979, 1980 and 1981 seasons?

6. Which freshman's team-best six picks during the 2022 season included a 96-yard interception return touchdown against Clemson?

7. Which Irish defensive back intercepted a hat-trick of passes in a New Year's Eve 2010 Sun Bowl win over Miami?

8. Which pass rusher returned a fumble 77 yards for a touchdown in a 2012 game against Navy?

9. Which linebacker registered 24.5 sacks, one interception and three forced fumbles between 2013 and 2015 before being drafted by the Dallas Cowboys?

10. Who is Notre Dame's all-time leader in career interceptions after picking off 17 passes between 1973 and 1977?

11. Which All-American defensive lineman from the 1960s later went on to become a judge on the Minnesota Supreme Court?

12. Which Irish defender scored 66 and 43-yard interception return touchdowns against Wisconsin and Georgia Tech during the 2021 season?

13. Which unanimous All-American defensive back tied a school record after scoring three interception return touchdowns between 1999 and 2002?

14. Who is the only Notre Dame defensive back to register more than 100 tackles in a season (he did it in both 2008 and 2009)?

15. Whose 13.5 sacks are the most by a Notre Dame defender in a single season?

16. Who are the two Irish defenders to register a record 26 tackles in a game?

17. Whose seven picks in 2012 are the most by a Notre Dame linebacker in a single season?

18. In 1975, which legendary Irish defender set the record for the most tackles by a Notre Dame freshman?

19. Who holds the team record for the most career sacks? a) Isaiah Foskey b) Justin Tuck c) Stephon Tuitt

20. How many sacks did he register to set that record? a) 26.5 b) 27.5 c) 28.5

Quiz 7 Answers

1. A leprechaun 2. Michigan State 3. Jeff Samardzija 4. Eight games 5. Losing 6. Clemson 7. Reggie Brooks 8. Steve Beuerlein 9. True 10. LSU 11. Calvin 12. Ricky Watters 13. Boston College 14. Marshall Thundering Herd 15. Wayne Bullock 16. Joe Theismann 17. Allen Pinkett 18. Winning 19. a) 77,622 20. c) 39 games

QUIZ 9 POT LUCK

1. In what decade did the Irish play their first game at Notre Dame Stadium?

2. The Leahy Memorial Bowl is the name of the trophy awarded to the winner of the game between Notre Dame and which opponent?

3. True or false – Former Irish receiver Equanimeous St. Brown is a fluent speaker of French and German?

4. Whose 1,921 career rushing yards are the most by a Notre Dame quarterback?

5. The Irish set a school record in 1993 after scoring 41 points in the second half of a game against which longtime rival?

6. Up to the close of the 2022 season, did the Irish have a winning or losing record in Bowl Games?

7. Which all-time great recovered a school record 12 fumbles in the mid-1970s?

8. Which linebacker recovered two fumbles in a 2008 game against Michigan, returning the second for a 35-yard touchdown to give the Irish a famous win over the Wolverines?

9. Which Notre Dame running back, who was injured while serving in the Vietnam War, went on to win four Super Bowls with the Pittsburgh Steelers?

10. In 1943, who became the first Irish player to win the Heisman Trophy?

11. Longtime Irish coach Lou Holtz spent a single season in the NFL as the head coach of which team?

12. In 1999, the Irish overturned a 24-3 third quarter deficit to beat which rival 25-24?

13. Which head coach suffered a torn ACL and a broken femur after accidentally colliding with a player in a 2008 game against Michigan?

14. Marcus Freeman's first game as Notre Dame head coach was a Bowl Game loss to which opponent?

15. Who passed for 5,805 yards and 47 touchdowns and rushed for 997 yards and 18 more touchdowns despite spending just two seasons at South Bend in the mid-2010s?

16. Which receiver caught 13 passes for 276 yards in his debut for the Irish against Purdue in 1966?

17. Who is the only Irish tight end to have been named a consensus All-American more than once?

18. What was special about Notre Dame's November1994 game against USC?

19. What is the largest victory in the history of Notre Dame football? a) 122-0 b) 132-0 c) 144-0

20. That lopsided win came against which opponent? a) American Educational b) American Legal c) American Medical

Quiz 8 Answers

1. Ross Browner 2. Isaiah Foskey 3. Justin Tuck 4. Mike Townsend 5. Bob Crable 6. Benjamin Morrison 7. Harrison Smith 8. Stephon Tuitt 9. Jaylon Smith 10. Luther Bradley 11. Alan Page 12. Jack Kiser 13. Shane Walton 14. Kyle McCarthy 15. Justin Tuck 16. Bob Crable and Bob Golic 17. Manti T'eo 18. Bob Golic 19. a) Isaiah Foskey 20. a) 26.5 sacks

QUIZ 10 SPECIAL TEAMS

1. In 2019, who became the first Notre Dame kicker to score 100 points in a season?

2. Who is the only Notre Dame player to score two kickoff return touchdowns in the same game more than once?

3. Whose 367 points between 2015 and 2018 are the most ever by a Notre Dame kicker?

4. Which Notre Dame defensive star blocked what would have been a game-winning field goal with just seconds remaining to give the Irish a famous 1979 win over Michigan?

5. Whose 97-yard punt return against SMU in 1989 is the longest in school history?

6. Which walk-on kicker achieved cult status after converting four field goals in a 19-17 win over Michigan in 1988?

7. Which future NFL star scored a 100-yard kickoff return touchdown in a September 2000 game against Nebraska?

8. Tim Brown is one of two Notre Dame players to score two punt return touchdowns in the same game. Which speedy defensive back is the other?

9. Which Notre Dame alum appeared in more than 300 games in an NFL career that stretched from 1988 to 2010?

10. Which kicker set a school record after converting 23 straight field goals across the 2009 and 2010 seasons?

11. Who returned a kickoff 98 yards for a touchdown in a 2021 game against Wisconsin?

12. How long is the longest successful field goal in school history?

13. Which kicker tied that record-long boot in a 2013 game against Arizona State?

14. Who holds the school record for the most career kickoff return touchdowns?

15. Who converted a school record 136 straight PATs between 1989 and 1992?

16. Who recovered a blocked punt and returned it for a 17-yard touchdown to open the scoring in a 2022 game against Clemson?

17. Who is the only Notre Dame player to score four kick and punt return touchdowns in a single season?

18. Of Notre Dame kickers to have converted at least 15 field goals, who has the best conversion percentage?

19. Who tied the school record for the most career punt return touchdowns after returning three between 2004 and 2007? a) Armando Allen b) Bennett Jackson c) Tom Zbikowski

20. The longest punt in school history was an 86-yard effort from whom? a) Bill Dickens b) Bill Faulkner c) Bill Shakespeare

Quiz 9 Answers

1. 1930s 2. Boston College 3. True 4. Tony Rice 5. Navy 6. Losing 7. Ross Browner 8. Brian Smith 9. Rocky Bleier 10. Angelo Bertelli 11. New York Jets 12. USC 13. Charlie Weis 14. Oklahoma State 15. DeShone Kizer 16. Jim Seymour 17. Ken MacAfee 18. It was their last tie 19. c) 144-0 20. c) American Medical

QUIZ 11 POT LUCK

1. What are the official colors of the Notre Dame Fighting Irish?

2. The Jeweled Shillelagh is awarded to the winner of games between Notre Dame and which Californian opponent?

3. Who was the last Notre Dame head coach to lead the team to a losing record in his first season in charge?

4. True or false – Notre Dame has produced more consensus All-Americans than any other college program?

5. Who rushed for a 97-yard touchdown in a 2018 game at Virginia Tech?

6. The Irish won the Orange Bowl for the second time in their history on New Year's Day 1990 after knocking off which #1 ranked opponent?

7. Which quarterback orchestrated a three-play, 80-yard drive with just over a minute on the clock to give the Irish a stunning 20-17 come-from-behind win over UCLA in 2006?

8. Who caught the game-winning 45-yard touchdown to seal that victory over UCLA?

9. Which opponent did Notre Dame face in their first ever Bowl Game appearance?

10. Which quarterback's first career touchdown pass came on a fake field goal in a classic 34-27 win over Virginia in 2015?

11. True or false – Up to the start of the 2023 season, the Irish had played in just 41 Bowl Games?

12. Which quarterback, who threw 61 touchdown passes for the Irish between 2010 and 2013, was named the offensive coordinator of the Alabama Crimson Tide in February 2023?

13. Which Notre Dame great from the 1950s was the first player to win the Maxwell Award, which is given to the best all-round player in college football, more than once?

14. Which defensive back was Notre Dame's only consensus All-American for 2021?

15. Which receiver, whose first name and surname start with the same letter, was the MVP of the 2019 Camping World Bowl against Iowa State after catching seven passes for 146 yards?

16. What is the fewest number of passes the Irish have completed in a single game?

17. True or false – The Irish didn't appear in postseason games from 1925 through to 1968?

18. Whose spectacular punt return touchdown with less than a minute remaining in the 1991 Orange Bowl against Colorado was chalked off because of a controversial clipping penalty?

19. In their early years the Irish played home games at which venue? a) Cartier Stadium b) Ratner Stadium c) Tiffany Stadium

20. Which opponent has Notre Dame faced the most times throughout its history? a) Army b) Navy c) Air Force

Quiz 10 Answers

1. Jonathan Doerer 2. Raghib Ismail 3. Justin Yoon 4. Bob Crable 5. Ricky Watters 6. Reggie Ho 7. Julius Jones 8. Allen Rossum 9. John Carney 10. David Ruffer 11. Chris Tyree 12. 53 yards 13. Kyle Brindza 14. Raghib Ismail 15. Craig Hentrich 16. Prince Kollie 17. Allen Rossum 18. Nick Tausch 19. c) Tom Zbikowski 20. c) Bill Shakespeare

QUIZ 12 ALL-TIME GREATS

1. Which Notre Dame great led the NFL in receptions in 1997?

2. Which quarterback had a 20-3-2 record as a starter for the Irish between 1968 and 1970?

3. Which Irish defensive lineman is fifth on the list of most all-time sacks for the Cincinnati Bengals. That total includes a sack of former teammate Joe Montana in Super Bowl XVI?

4. Which Notre Dame great scored one of the most controversial NFL touchdowns of all time in the play known as 'The Holy Roller'?

5. Which former Notre Dame star was the longtime holder of the NFL record for scoring the most points in a season until it was broken by LaDainian Tomlinson in 2006?

6. *The Winning Spirit: 16 Timeless Principles That Drive Performance Excellence* was written by which Notre Dame star?

7. Which Notre Dame legend released a CD in 2003 called *The Reign Cometh*?

8. Which Irish rusher has made a number of TV appearances including cameos in *The Office* and *Chuck*?

9. Which defensive tackle was a consensus All-American in both 1989 and 1990 and also UPI's Lineman of the Year for 1989?

10. Which pass rusher from the early 2000s is a cousin of NFL stars Bobby Wagner and Adalius Thomas?

11. Which linebacker started 47 straight games for the Irish from 2009 onward and registered 100 tackles in three consecutive seasons from 2010?

12. Which successful Notre Dame quarterback helped steer the Barcelona Dragons to the 1991 championship game in the World League of American Football?

13. In what country was the legendary Notre Dame coach Knute Rockne born?

14. Which Notre Dame and NFL defender is also a successful entrepreneur whose investments include a sunglasses brand, a mental health app and a ramen bar at Notre Dame Stadium?

15. In 1943, the US Navy launched a pair of Liberty ships that were named after which two former Notre Dame greats?

16. Which Heisman Trophy winner would often carry the flag of St. Patrick in Chicago's famous St. Patrick's Day parade?

17. Drafted by Washington in 1993, which Notre Dame alum broke the 1,000-yard barrier in his debut season in the pros and received All-Rookie recognition?

18. True or false – Heisman Trophy winner Angelo Bertelli was the father of Bob Bert, drummer with the rock band Sonic Youth?

19. What was running back Vagas Ferguson's given first name? a) Valentino b) Valerio c) Vasquero

20. What was the nickname of the versatile All-American Jim Martin? a) Jailer Jim b) Jumpin' Jim c) Jungle Jim

Quiz 11 Answers

1. Blue and gold 2. USC 3. Lou Holtz in 1986 4. True 5. Dexter Williams 6. Colorado 7. Brady Quinn 8. Jeff Samardzija 9. Stanford 10. Deshone Kizer 11. True 12. Tommy Rees 13. Johnny Lattner 14. Kyle Hamilton 15. Chase Claypool 16. Zero 17. True 18. Raghib Ismail 19. a) Cartier Stadium 20. b) Navy

QUIZ 13 POT LUCK

1. Notre Dame competes with which team to win The Legends Trophy?

2. Quarterback Sam Hartman transferred to Notre Dame from which school?

3. Which former Notre Dame defensive star was awarded the Presidential Medal of Freedom in 2018?

4. The longest reception in school history was a 96-yard touchdown against Georgia Tech in November 1981. Who caught it?

5. Which quarterback threw that record long pass?

6. True or false – The Irish have the best winning percentage by a Division I school in the history of college football?

7. Which opponent did the Irish face in a wintry November 1992 game nicknamed 'The Snow Bowl'?

8. Who caught a 2-point conversion with less than 30 seconds on the clock to give Notre Dame a 17-16 win in that game?

9. Which opponent did the Irish defeat 39-28 in the 1992 game nicknamed 'The Cheerios Bowl'?

10. True or false – Each Notre Dame helmet includes a flake of 23.9 carat gold?

11. Which versatile Notre Dame offensive weapon and future NFL star wrote the 2002 book *For Who For What, a Warrior's Journey*?

12. What number jersey did running back Jerome Bettis wear at Notre Dame?

13. Which safety, who was Notre Dame's MVP in 1982, was a key component on the all-time great Chicago Bears defense that won Super Bowl XX?

14. Which legend was the first Notre Dame player to receive All-American recognition?

15. Which offensive weapon was the only Notre Dame player named a consensus All-American for the 2022 season?

16. What is the highest number of sacks the Irish have registered in a single season?

17. What is the highest number of passes the the Irish have had intercepted in a single game?

18. True or false – The Irish were 0-3 in their first three games that went to overtime?

19. How much did Notre Dame Stadium originally cost to build? a) $75,000 b) $750,000 c) $7,500,000

20. Which opponent has the most victories in games against Notre Dame? a) Purdue b) USC c) Stanford

Quiz 12 Answers

1. Tim Brown 2. Joe Theismann 3. Ross Browner 4. Dave Casper 5. Paul Hornung 6. Joe Montana 7. Raghib Ismail 8. Jerome Bettis 9. Chris Zorich 10. Justin Tuck 11. Manti T'eo 12. Tony Rice 13. Norway 14. Jaylon Smith 15. George Gipp and Knute Rockne 16. Johnny Lattner 17. Reggie Brooks 18. True 19. c) Vasquero 20. c) Jungle Jim

QUIZ 14 COACHES

1. Which head coach has steered Notre Dame to the most wins?

2. Before joining the staff at Notre Dame, Marcus Freeman had spent the previous four seasons as the defensive coordinator at which program?

3. Brian Kelly surprisingly left Notre Dame to take over at which college?

4. Who was the head coach of the team that won the National Championship in 1966?

5. Which head coach holds the team record for the most unbeaten seasons?

6. Immediately prior to being appointed the head coach at Notre Dame Charlie Weis had been the offensive coordinator with which NFL team?

7. Which head coach has steered the team to the most losses as head coach?

8. Who was the head coach of the team that won National Championships in 1924, 1929 and 1930?

9. Which name is missing from this list? Dan Devine, ????, Lou Holtz, Bob Davie

10. Which head coach led Notre Dame to National Championship glory in 1977?

11. With 13 seasons in charge, who is Notre Dame's longest-serving head coach?

12. Who is the only head coach to win four National Championships with Notre Dame?

13. True or false – Marcus Freeman lost his first three games as Notre Dame's head coach?

14. Which 26-year-old succeeded Frank Leahy as the Fighting Irish head coach in 1954?

15. Who was the first Notre Dame head coach to lead the team to 100 wins?

16. Who is the only Notre Dame head coach to have lost nine games in a single season?

17. Who was the last Notre Dame head coach to have been born in the state of Indiana?

18. In 2001, who resigned just days after being appointed the Notre Dame head coach?

19. Which Notre Dame head coach has the best career win percentage? a) Frank Leahy b) Ara Parseghian c) Knute Rockne

20. Who was the last Notre Dame head coach with more than one losing season? a) Bob Davie b) Charlie Weis c) Tyrone Willingham

Quiz 13 Answers

1. Stanford 2. Wake Forest 3. Alan Page 4. Joe Howard 5. Blair Kiel 6. False 7. Penn State 8. Reggie Brooks 9. Florida 10. True 11. Ricky Watters 12. #6 13. Dave Duerson 14. George Gipp 15. Michael Mayer 16. 41 sacks 17. Eight 18. True 19. b) $750,000 20. b) USC

QUIZ 15 POT LUCK

1. In what year did the Irish play their first night game at Notre Dame Stadium?

2. The Irish defeated which opponent 23-17 in that famous first nighttime encounter?

3. Which fullback was carried off the field by his teammates following a 1995 win over the USC Trojans?

4. Which pair of Notre Dame backs from the early 1990s were known collectively as 'Thunder and Lightning'?

5. True or false – More players have been picked from Notre Dame than any other college in the history of the NFL Draft?

6. How many games did the Irish win in Marcus Freeman's first full season as head coach?

7. Which opponent did the Irish defeat in the 1979 contest known as 'The Chicken Soup Game'?

8. Which quarterback returned from his sickbed to throw a late 8-yard touchdown to give the Irish the win?

9. Who caught that famous pass?

10. What was the name of the Indiana State Policeman who delivered public safety announcements at Notre Dame Stadium for 55 years?

11. A nine-yard reverse touchdown run from which receiver gave the Irish their first ever overtime win in a 2000 game against Air Force?

12. The Irish tied a modern school record after scoring 69 points in a 1975 game against which then independent but now ACC school?

13. Which historical rival was the last opponent to shutout Notre Dame? (clue: it was in 2011)

14. Whose amazing one-handed catch and run for a touchdown gave the Irish a famous win over LSU in the 2018 Citrus Bowl?

15. Which quarterback, who'd come off the bench, threw that pass?

16. What is the campus mural whose official name is *The Word of Life* more commonly known?

17. Since 2000, who are the two Notre Dame wide receivers to receive consensus All-American honors?

18. True or false – Former Notre Dame defensive back Austin Collinsworth is the son of NFL broadcaster Cris Collinsworth?

19. In what year did the Irish play their first Spring Game? a) 1922 b) 1932 c) 1942

20. The first win in school history came against which opponent? a) Harvard Prep School of Chicago b) Navy c) Purdue

Quiz 14 Answers

1. Brian Kelly 2. Cincinnati 3. LSU 4. Ara Parseghian 5. Knute Rockne 6. New England 7. Brian Kelly 8. Knute Rockne 9. Gerry Faust 10. Dan Devine 11. Knute Rockne 12. Frank Leahy 13. True 14. Terry Brennan 15. Knute Rockne 16. Charlie Weis 17. Joe Kuharich 18. George O'Leary 19. c) Knute Rockne 20. a) Bob Davie

QUIZ 16 1988 NATIONAL CHAMPIONS

1. Who was the head coach of the team that was crowned the 1988 National Champion?

2. The Irish sealed the National Championship with a win over which opponent in the Fiesta Bowl?

3. That Fiesta Bowl was hosted in which city?

4. With 700 yards and nine touchdowns who was the leading rusher in 1988?

5. Who led the team with 331 receiving yards despite catching just 12 passes in 1988?

6. Notre Dame opened the season with a famous 19-17 win over which nationally ranked Big 10 opponent?

7. The only Irish touchdown in that season-opener came courtesy of an 81-yard punt return from which player?

8. Which defensive lineman led the team with 7.5 sacks during the 1988 season?

9. Notre Dame brought which number one ranked opponent's 36-game regular season winning streak to a close in a classic week six encounter?

10. What was the final score in that contest which was dubbed *The Game of the Century*?

11. Which linebacker recovered a Cleveland Gary fumble at the Notre Dame 2-yard line midway through the fourth quarter of that epic game?

12. #1 ranked Notre Dame defeated which #2 ranked PAC-10 opponent 27-10 in the penultimate game of the season?

13. True or false – The Irish didn't give up more than 20 points in a game throughout the whole of the 1988 season?

14. Whose 836 all-purpose yards were the most by a Notre Dame player in 1988?

15. Which All-American offensive tackle from the National Championship-winning team was drafted by the Seattle Seahawks with the 15th overall pick of the 1989 NFL Draft?

16. Who was the offensive coordinator on the 1988 team?

17. Tony Rice was one of two Irish quarterbacks to throw a touchdown pass during the 1988 season. Who was the other?

18. Who was the defensive coordinator on the 1988 team?

19. How many points did the Irish concede throughout the season? a) 146 b) 156 c) 166

20. The Irish started the 1988 season ranked at what position on the AP Poll? a) 10th b) 13th c) 16th

Quiz 15 Answers

1. 1982 2. Michigan 3. Marc Edwards 4. Jerome Bettis and Reggie Brooks 5. True 6. Nine 7. Houston 8. Joe Montana 9. Kris Haines 10. Sgt. Tim McCarthy 11. Joey Getherall 12. Georgia Tech 13. Boston College 14. Miles Boykin 15. Ian Book 16. Touchdown Jesus 17. Jeff Samardzija and Golden Tate 18. True 19. a) 1922 20. a) Harvard Prep School of Chicago

QUIZ 17 POT LUCK

1. Whose 23 career rushing touchdowns are the most by a Notre Dame quarterback?

2. President Ronald Reagan played which Notre Dame star in the movie *Knute Rockne, All American*?

3. Which defensive end was the last Notre Dame player taken with the first overall pick of the NFL Draft? (clue – it was in the 1970s)

4. Do the Irish have an all-time winning or losing record in road games?

5. Measuring 6ft 5in and weighing 260 pounds, which Notre Dame star is the largest player to have won the Heisman Trophy?

6. What number jersey did Paul Hornung wear while at Notre Dame?

7. Which freshman rushed for a 76-yard touchdown as unranked Notre Dame shocked Dan Marino and the #1 ranked Pitt Panthers 31-16 in November 1982?

8. True or false – The first ever edition of *College Gameday* hosted on the road was at Notre Dame Stadium?

9. Who has been the main play-by-play commentator on Notre Dame radio broadcasts since 2018?

10. Which former Irish o-lineman and Super Bowl winner with Denver is his regular color co-commentator?

11. In 1991, the Irish blew a 31-7 lead, having two field goals blocked in the process, before going on to lose 35-34 to which opponent?

12. 'Running' was the nickname of which Notre Dame offensive star from the late 1980s and early 1990s?

13. Which kicker on the 1973 National Championship team went on to spend more than a decade in the NFL before becoming a justice on the Supreme Court of Illinois?

14. Who was Notre Dame's first African-American head coach?

15. Who was the last Notre Dame offensive player to be named a consensus All-American in back-to-back seasons?

16. Which tight end, who caught 100 passes for the Irish between 2004 and 2007, later played in the NFL for Seattle, Minnesota and Arizona, catching 210 passes and 15 TDs?

17. True or false – Every game at Notre Dame Stadium between September 1974 and November 2023 was a sell out?

18. What is the most touchdowns the Irish have scored in a single game?

19. In what year did the first Notre Dame football game take place? a) 1877 b) 1887 c) 1897

20. Which opponent did the Irish face in that first ever game? a) Michigan b) Ohio State c) Yale

Quiz 16 Answers

1. Lou Holtz 2. West Virginia 3. Tempe, Arizona 4. Tony Rice 5. Raghib Ismail 6. Michigan 7. Ricky Watters 8. Frank Stams 9. Miami (Fl.) 10. Fighting Irish 31-30 Hurricanes 11. Michael Stonebreaker 12. USC 13. False 14. Raghib Ismail 15. Andy Heck 16. Jim Strong 17. Steve Belles 18. Barry Alvarez 19. b) 156 points 20. b) 13th

QUIZ 18 FIGHTING IRISH IN THE NFL

1. Which bruising back was drafted 10th overall by the Rams in 1993 but is better known for his stellar 10-year stint in Pittsburgh?

2. Which Notre Dame alum was named the NFL MVP for the 1983 season?

3. Which Dallas guard received All-Pro recognition in eight of his first nine seasons in the NFL?

4. Tim Brown spent 16 years with the Raiders and one season with which NFC team?

5. Which Heisman Trophy winner was named the NFL MVP for 1961 and was a member of the Packers team that won the first Super Bowl?

6. Which former Notre Dame tight end caught his 50th career NFL touchdown pass in a 2022 game for the Bucs against the Falcons?

7. After winning three Super Bowls in San Francisco, Joe Montana spent the final two seasons of his NFL career with which team?

8. Which safety appeared in 159 games for the Vikings between 2012 and 2022, intercepting 34 passes, forcing 9 fumbles and scoring four touchdowns?

9. Which former Notre Dame receiver enjoyed 1,000-yard seasons with Detroit in 2014, 2016 and 2017?

10. Which defensive lineman, who won two Super Bowls with the Giants, went on to have a career on Wall Street with banking giant Goldman Sachs?

11. Which former Irish star set an NFL postseason record after scoring five rushing touchdowns in the San Francisco 49ers' 44-3 rout of the New York Giants in January 1994?

12. In 1971, which former Notre Dame great became the first defensive player to win the NFL MVP Award?

13. The Indianapolis Colts used the sixth overall pick of the 2018 NFL Draft to select which Notre Dame offensive guard?

14. 'The Ghost' was the nickname of which former Notre Dame tight end who was named on the NFL's All-Decade Team for the 1970s?

15. Which Irish quarterback went 1-9 as a starter in his NFL rookie season with Carolina in 2010?

16. 'The Mad Bomber' was the nickname of which quarterback who started three seasons at Notre Dame and later found success in the NFL with the Bills and Raiders?

17. Which Notre Dame quarterback won two Super Bowl rings as Terry Bradshaw's backup on the great Pittsburgh Steelers teams of the 1970s?

18. Which Irish offensive superstar enjoyed his only 1,000-yard receiving season in the pros with the Cardinals in 2013?

19. Which Notre Dame great's 12th and final NFL touchdown pass was thrown to Kansas City's Jonathan Baldwin in a 2012 win over the Panthers?

20. Which linebacker and Notre Dame co-captain from the 1960s won two Super Bowls with Miami in the 1970s and was elected into the Pro Football Hall of Fame in 2001?

Quiz 17 Answers

1. Tony Rice 2. George Gipp 3. Walt Patulski 4. Winning 5. Leon Hart 6. #5 7. Allen Pinkett 8. True 9. Paul Burmeister 10. Ryan Harris 11. Tennessee 12. Ricky Watters 13. Bob Thomas 14. Tyrone Willingham 15. Aaron Taylor 16. John Carlson 17. False 18. 27 TDs 19. b) 1887 20. a) Michigan

QUIZ 19 POT LUCK

1. Who was the last head coach to steer the team to a losing season?

2. 'The Holy War' is the nickname of the rivalry between Notre Dame and which opponent?

3. In 1977, which tight end became the first Notre Dame player to win the Walter Camp Award which is given to the nation's outstanding college football player?

4. #2 ranked Notre Dame survived a late rally to defeat which #1 ranked opponent 31-24 in November 1993?

5. Which cornerback batted down a pass at the goal line to secure that famous victory?

6. In July 2009, the Irish played a game in which Asian capital?

7. Notre Dame featured in the first nationally-televised game in the history of college football. In what decade did that first broadcast air?

8. Which Big 12 opponent did the Irish face in that inaugural televised game?

9. Which of the two Golic brothers is older – Bob or Mike?

10. The Irish were involved in a 0-0 tie in a 1946 game against which branch of the military?

11. That 0-0 tie was hosted at which baseball stadium?

12. True or false – Former Irish stars Tyler Eifert and Zack Martin are brothers-in-law?

13. Which Notre Dame tight end, who was drafted by the Giants in 1985, would go on to win two Super Bowls and would twice be named an All-Pro?

14. Which Notre Dame guard and member of the College Football Hall of Fame was part of the Green Bay team that won Super Bowl XXXI?

15. Who was the last Notre Dame head coach to go 8-0 in his first eight games in charge?

16. Notre Dame alum J.J. Jansen holds the record for the most games played by a Carolina Panther. What position does he play?

17. During the 1980 season, Notre Dame held their opponents without a touchdown for how many straight quarters?

18. What was Curly Lambeau's given first name?

19. In what year did the Irish register their first perfect season? a) 1903 b) 1913 c) 1923

20. The Irish defeated which opponent in the first ever game played at Notre Dame Stadium? a) Navy b) SMU c) USC

Quiz 18 Answers

1. Jerome Bettis 2. Joe Theismann 3. Zack Martin 4. Tampa Bay 5. Paul Hornung 6. Kyle Rudolph 7. Kansas City Chiefs 8. Harrison Smith 9. Golden Tate 10. Justin Tuck 11. Ricky Watters 12. Alan Page 13. Quenton Nelson 14. Dave Casper 15. Jimmy Clausen16. Daryle Lamonica 17. Terry Hanratty 18. Michael Floyd 19. Brady Quinn 20. Nick Buoniconti

QUIZ 20 NUMBERS GAME

What number jersey did the following players wear while at Notre Dame?

1. Tim Brown and Miles Boykin

2. Brady Quinn and Drew Pyne

3. Joe Montana and Rick Mirer

4. John Carney and Joey Getherall

5. Julius Jones and Harrison Smith

6. Golden Tate and Autry Denson

7. Rocket Ismail and Chris Tyree

8. Kyle Hamilton and DeShone Kizer

9. Ricky Watters and Ian Book

10. Alan Page and Ken MacAfee

11. Justin Tuck and Tom Gatewood

12. Ross Browner and John Carlson

13. Allen Pinkett and Luther Bradley

14. Tom Clements and Reggie Ho

15. Kory Minor and Ryan Grant

16. Jeff Samardzija and Chase Claypool

17. Aaron Taylor and Tim Grunhard

18. Tony Rice and Kyle Rudolph

19. Joe Theismann and Jimmy Clausen

20. Manti T'eo and Everett Golson

Quiz 19 Answers

1. Brian Kelly 2. Boston College 3. Ken MacAfee 4. Florida State 5. Shawn Wooden 6. Tokyo 7. 1950s 8. Oklahoma 9. Bob 10. Army 11. Yankee Stadium 12. True 13. Mark Bavaro 14. Aaron Taylor 15. Tyrone Willingham 16. Long snapper 17. 23 quarters 18. Earl 19. b) 1913 20. b) SMU

QUIZ 21 POT LUCK

1. Which team selected Brady Quinn in the first round of the 2007 NFL Draft?

2. During the 1990s and early 2000s the Irish lost how many Bowl Games in a row?

3. Which Notre Dame defender received the 2020 Butkus Award which is given to the top linebacker in college football?

4. True or false – The Irish won 28 straight home games between 1942 and 1950?

5. The 6-0 Irish secured a famous 20-13 win over which opponent in October 2012 courtesy of an epic goal line stand?

6. Which domineering defender's 77 career tackles for a loss are the most by a Notre Dame player?

7. Which tight end famously caught a pass in the 1991 season opener against Indiana and dragged a pair of Hoosier defenders with him to the end zone for a spectacular 58-yard touchdown?

8. In 1985, Lou Holtz left which college to become the head coach at Notre Dame?

9. Which grad student safety appeared in a record 61st game for Notre Dame in the 2022 Gator Bowl against South Carolina?

10. Which Notre Dame defensive lineman from the early 1990s was inducted into the Pro Football Hall of Fame in 2021 after a stellar career with the 49ers?

11. True or false – The Irish were never shutout during Brian Kelly's tenure as head coach?

12. What is the highest number of two-point conversions the Irish have successfully converted in a single game?

13. Which Notre Dame quarterback's NFL career ran from 1987 to 2003 and included 24,000 yards and 147 touchdown passes?

14. Bob Golic received All-American recognition in football and what other sport?

15. Complete the nickname of Notre Dame's dominant offensive backfield from the 1920s – The Four...?

16. The Irish suffered a controversial loss in 2005 to which opponent in the contest known as 'The Bush Push Game'?

17. Brothers and Notre Dame alums Julian and Romeo Okwara both played for which NFL team during the 2022 season?

18. In 1975, which future all-time great with the Dallas Cowboys became the first running back to rush for more than 300 yards in a game against Notre Dame?

19. What is the most yards the Irish have amassed in a single game? a) 700 yards b) 710 yards c) 720 yards

20. The Irish secured a famous 8-7 win over Purdue in 1971 courtesy of what play? a) The Genuflect Play b) The Kneel Play c) The Hope and Pray Play

Quiz 20 Answers

1. #81 2. #10 3. #3 4. #18 5. #22 6. #23 7. #25 8. #14 9. #12 10. #81 11. #44 12. #89 13. #20 14. #2 15. #4 16. #83 17. #75 18. #9 19. #7 20. #5

QUIZ 22 ANAGRAMS (OFFENSE)

R earrange the letters to make the name of a Notre Dame offensive star.

1. Brim Town
2. Boa Ikon
3. Sunday Tenor
4. Jet Emits Robe
5. Go Talented
6. Chiefly Modal
7. Jean Man Too
8. Hulk Old Prey
9. Retry Leftie
10. Crank Ma Zit
11. Irish Mailbag
12. Lunar Gun Hop
13. Rye Tonic
14. Eclair Mayhem
15. Wackier Tryst
16. Cinema July Ms
17. Irk Mr Rice

18. Matinees John

19. Fazed If Jam Jars

20. Nor at a Royal

Quiz 21 Answers

1. Cleveland 2. Nine 3. Jeremiah Owusu-Koramoah 4. True 5. Stanford 6. Ross Browner 7. Irv Smith 8. University of Minnesota 9. Houston Griffith 10. Bryant Young 11. True 12. Two 13. Steve Beuerlein 14. Wrestling 15. Horsemen 16. USC 17. Detroit 18. Tony Dorsett 19. c) 720 yards 20. a) The Genuflect Play

QUIZ 23 POT LUCK

1. Who holds the record for the most career interceptions thrown by a Fighting Irish quarterback?

2. What is the highest number of games the Irish have lost in a single season?

3. Fighting Irish safety Kyle Hamilton was born in which European country?

4. Who is the only Notre Dame player to receive the Biletnikoff Award which is given to the top receiver in college football?

5. Which opponent did the Irish defeat 31-30 in the 1988 game known as 'Catholics versus Convicts'?

6. Which Notre Dame legend from the 1940s had a record of 20-1-1 when starting at quarterback for the Irish?

7. Which fullback barreled through a procession of Purdue defenders en route to a spectacular 62-yard touchdown in a 1994 game against the Boilermakers?

8. Best known as a Hall of Fame tight end, which versatile star from the early 1970s also played wide receiver, offensive tackle and defensive tackle while at Notre Dame?

9. True or false – Since 2000, the Irish are unbeaten in games when they have rushed for 200 yards or more?

10. In 1993, which Notre Dame guard won the Lombardi Award, which is given to the college football player "who best embodies the values and spirit of the NFL's legendary coach Vince Lombardi"?

11. Which safety recovered a fumble and returned it for a 96-yard touchdown in a losing effort against Michigan State in 1998?

12. Who rushed for a 94-yard touchdown in a December 2020 game against Syracuse?

13. Which safety intercepted seven passes in his final two seasons with the Irish before being drafted by Denver in 2008 where he became the special teams captain and won a Super Bowl ring in 2015?

14. Which shutdown corner from the 1988 National Championship team, who later won a Super Bowl with the Rams, was born in the Marshall Islands in the Pacific Ocean?

15. Who made his debut as commentator on NBC's television broadcasts of Notre Dame games during the 2022 season?

16. Which former NFL head coach joined him in the booth in 2022?

17. The Irish opened the 2012 season with a game in which European capital?

18. Which opponent did the Irish defeat by a score of 50-10 in that famous European encounter?

19. In 2011, Notre Dame was involved in a game that took six hours to complete. What was the reason for the delays to the game? a) A swarm of bees on the field b) Lightning strikes c) Waterlogged field

20. Which team defeated the Irish 23-20 in that epic six-hour matchup? a) Florida b) Florida State c) USF

Quiz 22 Answers

1. Tim Brown 2. Ian Book 3. Autry Denson 4. Jerome Bettis 5. Golden Tate 6. Michael Floyd 7. Joe Montana 8. Kyle Rudolph 9. Tyler Eifert 10. Zack Martin 11. Raghib Ismail 12. Paul Hornung 13. Tony Rice 14. Michael Mayer 15. Ricky Watters 16. Jimmy Clausen 17. Rick Mirer 18. Joe Theismann 19. Jeff Samardzija 20. Aaron Taylor

QUIZ 24 ANAGRAMS (DEFENSE)

R earrange the letters to make the name of a Notre Dame defensive star.

1. Nap Algae

2. Cut Sink Jut

3. Bobble Car

4. Saki If So Yeah

5. Hottest Input

6. Roomy Rink

7. Nor Browsers

8. Anvil Joule

9. Minor Shah Stir

10. Into Team

11. Jointly Mash

12. Terry Bullhead

13. Cubic Ink Notion

14. Adored Venus

15. Angry Bounty

16. Milky Ethanol

17. Much Winded Nuke

18. Travel Rows

19. Minor Miners Banjo

20. Ali Walks Putt

Quiz 23 Answers

1. Steve Beuerlein 2. Nine 3. Greece 4. Golden Tate 5. Miami Hurricanes 6. Johnny Lujack 7. Ray Zellars 8. Dave Casper 9. False 10. Aaron Taylor 11. Deke Cooper 12. Chris Tyree 13. David Bruton 14. Todd Lyght 15. Jac Collinsworth 16. Jason Garrett 17. Dublin 18. Navy 19. b) Lightning strikes 20. c) USF

QUIZ 25 POT LUCK

1. Which former Fighting Irish quarterback won the Grey Cup in the Canadian Football League in 2006, 2011 and 2012?

2. The Notre Dame school motto is the Latin *Vita, Dulcedo, Spes*. What does that translate into in English?

3. The Irish are holders of the NCAA record for the most consecutive wins against the same opponent. Which one?

4. What color are the facemasks on the Notre Dame helmet?

5. Who is the only Notre Dame player to receive the Mackey Award which is given to the nation's top collegiate tight end?

6. In November 1957, Notre Dame snapped which opponent's 47-game winning streak courtesy of a 7-0 victory?

7. Which junior's 25.8 yards per catch average (plus six TDs) in 2004 is the best by a Notre Dame receiver in a single season?

8. Who returned an interception for a 27-yard touchdown to give the Irish a famous 40-37 win over Michigan State in 2006, a game they had been losing 17-0?

9. Lou Holtz's final game as head coach of the Irish in 1996 was a 62-0 win over which opponent?

10. True or false – During the 2022 season the Irish blocked a punt in five straight games?

11. Which Notre Dame legend appeared in the TV sitcom, *Saved By The Bell: The College Years*?

12. What logo appeared on the side of the Notre Dame helmet for the first time in 1959?

13. Which former Notre Dame quarterback has made cameo acting appearances in TV shows and movies including *Cannonball Run 2, B.J. and the Bear* and *Brooklyn Nine-Nine*?

14. In September 2021, the Irish faced Wisconsin at which famous NFL stadium?

15. Who returned a kickoff for a 96-yard touchdown in that game?

16. In 1989, who became the first Notre Dame quarterback to win the Johnny Unitas Golden Arm Award winner?

17. Which NFL all-time great was one and done as a color co-commentator on Notre Dame TV broadcasts in 2021?

18. True or false – The most times the Irish have fumbled in a single game is ten?

19. Notre Dame has a winning record against which of the following teams? a) Florida State b) Ohio State c) Texas A&M

20. The dominant offensive linemen from the 1920s teams were known collectively as 'The Seven...'? a) Donkeys b) Horses c) Mules

Quiz 24 Answers

1. Alan Page 2. Justin Tuck 3. Bob Crable 4. Isaiah Foskey 5. Stephon Tuitt 6. Kory Minor 7. Ross Browner 8. Julian Love 9. Harrison Smith 10. Manti T'eo 11. Jaylon Smith 12. Luther Bradley 13. Nick Buoniconti 14. Dave Duerson 15. Bryant Young 16. Kyle Hamilton 17. Chindeum Ndukwe 18. Trevor Laws 19. Benjamin Morrison 20. Walt Patulski

ACKNOWLEDGEMENTS

Many thanks to designer extraordinaire Graham Nash, Heidi Grant, Stuart Kennedy, Bill Rankin, Ken and Veronica Bradshaw, Steph, James, Ben and Will Roe.

ABOUT THE AUTHOR

Chris Bradshaw has written more than 30 quiz book including titles on the NFL, college football, golf, tennis, Formula One, Moto GP and cycling. He has also written on cricket for The Times (of London) as well as on soccer, darts and poker.

ALSO BY CHRIS BRADSHAW

Ohio State Buckeyes Trivia Quiz Book

Philadelphia Eagles Trivia Quiz Book

Pittsburgh Steelers Trivia Quiz Book

San Francisco 49ers Trivia Quiz Book

Seattle Seahawks Trivia Quiz Book

Tampa Bay Buccaneers Trivia Quiz Book

Washington Commanders Trivia Quiz Book

Georgia Bulldogs Trivia Quiz Book

Michigan Wolverines Trivia Quiz Book

The Times Cricket Quiz Book

The Sun Darts Quiz Book

Made in the USA
Monee, IL
21 December 2023

50336217R00038